The diary of Thami the truck driver

written by Annecke

illustrated by Campbell

NEW READERS PUBLISHERS

About this book

Readers asked New Readers Publishers for a book about other countries. They said they wanted to learn some history and geography and how to read maps. Readers said they wanted to learn about the people in other countries. Here is a book which tells you a little bit about four countries and the people who live in them. The story is told by a truck driver called Thami. He writes a diary every night in which he describes the things he has seen while he drives through Zimbabwe, Zambia, Malawi and Mozambique. The book also has maps of these countries so you can follow the road he takes.

Introduction

My name is Thami and I am a long distance truck driver. Usually I take loads from Durban to Zimbabwe, but last month I did a special trip from Durban to Zimbabwe, then all the way through to Zambia. From Zambia I drove to Malawi and from there to Mozambique and back to Durban. It took more than a week. I got really tired of driving. But I was happy that I saw those countries. Before that, I had only heard their names.

It started when my boss called me into his office. He told me that the company wanted to expand into countries north of South Africa. They needed to know what the roads were like and where they must set up depots. He said that he had chosen me to find out these things, because I am the best truck driver in the company.

He said, "You must load up in Durban with supplies for Zimbabwe and Zambia. After you have unloaded some of these in Harare, the capital of Zimbabwe, you must go to Zambia.

After offloading in Lusaka, the capital of Zambia, you will drive to Lilongwe in Malawi. From Lilongwe you will drive to Maputo in Mozambique before coming home to Durban." I had never done such a long trip, but I was pleased to be chosen.

It is hard work being a truck driver. Sometimes you have to drive all day and at night. A driver gets very tired watching the road the whole time. You have to watch for cars coming from the front and from behind you. In the day the sun shines in your eyes, and at night the lights from the other cars blind you. You get stiff and sore from sitting for a long time. A big truck costs a lot of money so you have to look after it. Whatever you are carrying also costs a lot of money. It is a great responsibility to be a truck driver.

I said I would like to drive to all those places, Zimbabwe, Zambia, Malawi and Mozambique. I went home to tell my wife and children. My children were happy. They said I was an 'international' father. My son, Vusi, wanted to know where all those places were and how I could drive there. He thought I would have to fly over the sea in an aeroplane. I told him these countries were our neighbours in Africa. My daughter, Thandi, went to get her school geography book. "Here," she said, "we can see on a map where you are going."

We all looked at the book. We found a map of Africa. We found South Africa, Zimbabwe, Zambia, Malawi and Mozambique on the map. The book showed us the big towns I would be going to in each country:

Harare in Zimbabwe
Lusaka in Zambia
Lilongwe in Malawi
and Maputo in Mozambique.

The countries looked so small. We looked for a bigger map which showed us the main roads. We could see the road from Durban to Johannesburg and then to Musina. Thandi found where I would cross the border from South Africa into Zimbabwe. It was at Beit Bridge.

Morocco

Western Sahara

Alger

Mauritania

Mali

Senegal

The Gambia

Guinea-Bissau

Guinea

Burkina Faso

Sierra Leone

Liberia

Cote d'Ivoire

Ghana

Togo

Benin

ATLANTIC OCEAN

Tunisia

Libya

Egypt

Niger

Chad

Eritrea

Nigeria

Sudan

Djibouti

Cameroon

Central
African Republic

Ethiopia

Gabon

Somalia

Congo

Uganda

Democratic Republic of
the Congo (DRC)

Kenya

Rwanda
Burundi

Tanzania

Angola

Malawi

INDIAN OCEAN

Zambia

Namibia

Zimbabwe

Mozambique

Madagascar

Botswana

Swaziland

South Africa

Lesotho

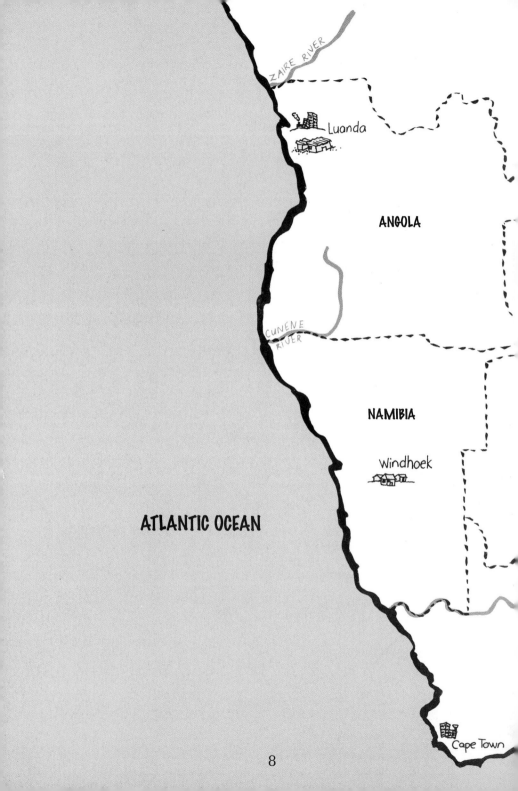

ZAIRE RIVER

Luanda

ANGOLA

CUNENE RIVER

NAMIBIA

Windhoek

ATLANTIC OCEAN

Cape Town

DEMOCRATIC REPUBLIC OF THE CONGO (DRC)

MALAWI

MOZAMBIQUE

ZAMBIA

Lusaka

Lilongwe

ZAMBEZI RIVER

Blantyre

Harare

ZIMBABWE

BOTSWANA

LIMPOPO RIVER

Gaberone

Pretoria

Johannesburg

Maputo

INDIAN OCEAN

Maseru

Durban

ORANGE RIVER

SOUTH AFRICA

Every night, until it was time for me to go, we did not watch TV. We were too busy looking at maps. We found the road I would take when I left Beit Bridge. The road went over the Limpopo River which is the border between South Africa and Zimbabwe. When I got into Zimbabwe, I had to take the road past Masvingo to Harare. From Harare I had to drive north west to Chirundu. From Chirundu I would cross into Zambia.

I was looking forward to going. There were many things to do first. My passport was checked. I went to the City Health Department. I had to have yellow fever and cholera injections to be safe in Zambia. The day before I left, I had to take pills which would help me against malaria. The company gave me different money for each country: Zimbabwean dollars, Zambian kwachas, Malawian kwachas and meticals for Mozambique.

The night before I had to leave, I packed a small bag with clean clothes and things to wash with. I also had a small stove to make tea or coffee.

Vusi and Thandi gave me a book and a pen. They asked me to write a diary every night. They wanted me to read it to them when I got back so they would know everything I did. I put my diary with my map book which told me useful things about each country.

I said I would write in my diary every night and read it to them when I got back. This is what I wrote.

Monday, South Africa

I got up when it was still dark. I washed and took my small bag and box. When I got to work the truck was ready. It was a nice big truck. It was not slow. I signed the logbook and said goodbye. The sun was just beginning to come up.

I drove from Durban to Johannesburg. The road to Pietermaritzburg is always bad. I moved to the left side of the road so that small, fast cars could pass me. Some people, especially Mercedes drivers and taxis, are very rude. Luckily it is not easy to push a big lorry around.

After Johannesburg I took the road to the north. I drove past Pretoria, Bela-bela, Modimolle, Naboomspruit. Hayi! If you think there are a lot of taxis on the road to Umlazi, you should see this road! The Gauteng drivers are so reckless. They overtake on a solid white line without thinking of the oncoming traffic.

Now I am at Polokwane. It is late and dark so I have stopped for the night. I found a place to

park the truck near the caravan park. I bought
meat and phutu at a café and made coffee.
Now I am going to bed. I must be at the border
early tomorrow, because there are a lot of forms
to fill in before you can go through. It is still
quite far to Musina, and Beitbridge is after
Musina.

It has taken me too long to write all this.
Tomorrow I will write just a few lines.

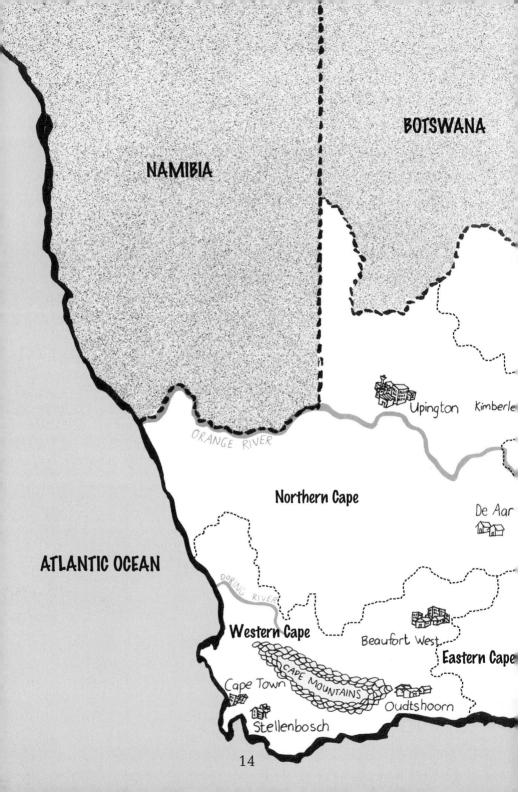

BOTSWANA

NAMIBIA

Upington   Kimberle

ORANGE RIVER

Northern Cape

De Aar

ATLANTIC OCEAN

DORING RIVER

Western Cape

Beaufort West

Eastern Cape

CAPE MOUNTAINS

Cape Town

Oudtshoorn

Stellenbosch

14

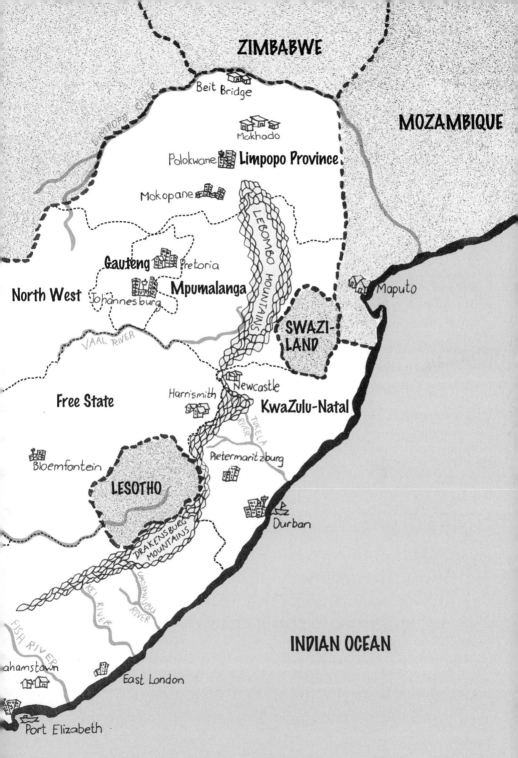

ZIMBABWE

MOZAMBIQUE

Beit Bridge

Makhado

Polokwane Limpopo Province

Mokopane

LEBOMBO MOUNTAINS

Gauteng Pretoria

North West Mpumalanga

Johannesburg

Maputo

VAAL RIVER

SWAZI-
LAND

Free State Harrismith Newcastle

KwaZulu-Natal

TUKELA RIVER

Bloemfontein Pietermaritzburg

LESOTHO

Durban

DRAKENSBURG MOUNTAINS

UMSIMKUBU RIVER

KEI RIVER

FISH RIVER

INDIAN OCEAN

ahamstown

East London

Port Elizabeth

15

Tuesday, Zimbabwe

I woke up early and used a cold water tap to wash. I did not make tea because I was in a hurry to get to the border.

There were already three trucks ahead of me when I stopped at the border post. It was not yet 5.30am. The border opened at 6am. The three drivers had slept there the night. They had made a small fire at the side of the road and were boiling water for tea. They called to me, "Hey, ND boy! Do you want some tea?" Hawu! They are so cheeky these guys from the Western Cape and Gauteng.

We drank tea. After a while the officials arrived to open the office. Hey! It takes a long time to fill in all the forms and do all the right things. First they checked me. Then they checked the truck. They checked the engine number with the logbook to make sure the truck was not stolen. They also checked the cargo.

They went through the cargo to see if I was carrying something illegal. There were young men in uniform doing the checking. Some of the other truck drivers got angry at the long time they had to wait. I tried to take it easy. I still had a lot of border posts to go through.

When I was finished on the South African side of the border, I drove across the bridge over the Limpopo River. This is the big river that divides Zimbabwe from South Africa. Sometimes it is full of water, but sometimes, like now, when there has been no rain, it is just a few pools with little water.

On the other side of the river was the Zimbabwean border post. The customs officials were dressed in blue pants and white shirts. They were friendly to me. One had even been to Durban, and he liked to swim in the sea. He spoke English to me. When he spoke to his friend, I could not understand what he was saying. This man told me that the Zimbabweans are very strict. They have to see that people do not take too much money out of the country. He checked my papers all over again.

At last I was through customs and on my way. I still had to drive to Harare, the capital city of

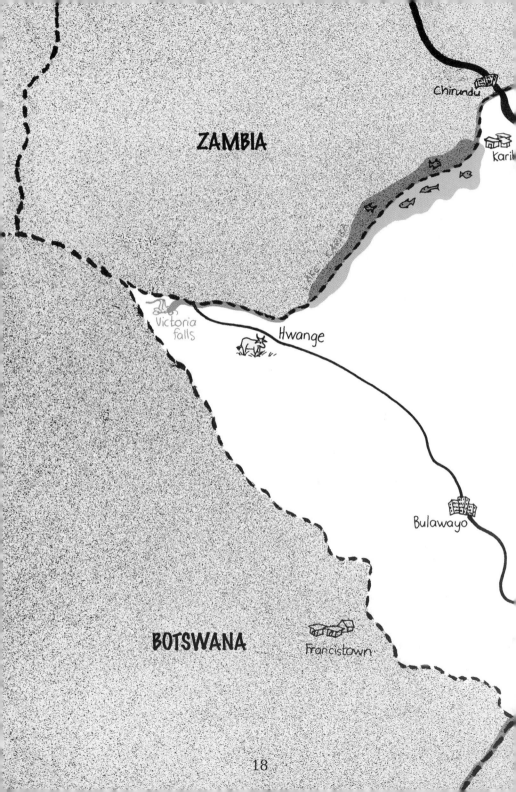

ZAMBIA

Chirundu

Kari

Victoria
falls

Hwange

Bulawayo

BOTSWANA

Francistown

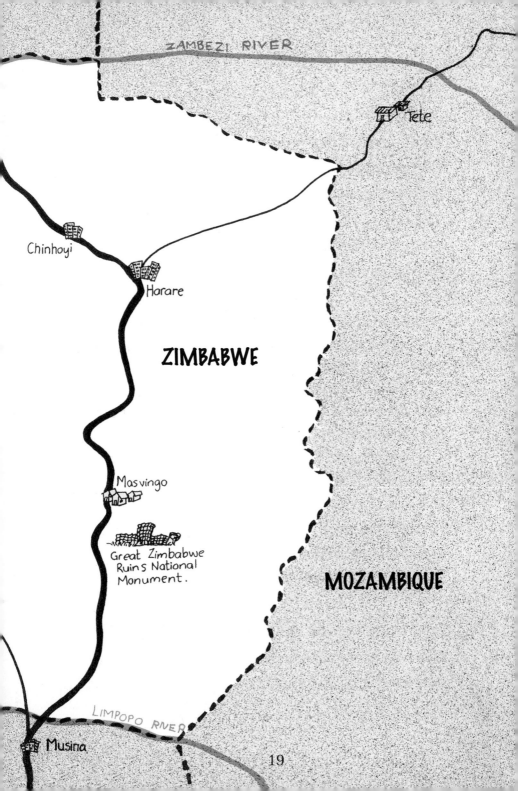

ZAMBEZI RIVER

Tete

Chinhoyi

Harare

ZIMBABWE

Masvingo

Great Zimbabwe
Ruins National
Monument.

MOZAMBIQUE

LIMPOPO RIVER

Musina

Zimbabwe. That is where I am now. On my way I passed Masvingo and the turn off to Lake Kyle and the Zimbabwe Ruins.

Tonight I read in my book about the Great Zimbabwe Ruins:

> Many hundreds of years ago (between the 11th and 15th centuries), people called the Karanga built a huge city of stone. There were up to 30,000 people living in this city. It had huge, high walls all around it and a place in the middle where the king lived. The people grew crops and traded gold with others coming to and from the coast.

I was sorry I did not have time to go and see these great *dzimba dzembabwe,* or houses of stone as the book called them.

I drove all the way to Harare. My body was stiff and sore from sitting all day. When I got here, I was tired and dirty and hungry. I found a good place to park my truck. I went to look for something to eat.

Some parts of Harare are very pretty. In town the roads are very wide with trees down the middle. I enjoyed the cool night air. The weather in Harare is like Johannesburg except that it is not so cold in winter.

I heard loud music coming from shebeens in the poor area, but I did not go into any. Instead, I found a hotel with a beer garden. I asked for a beer.

I talked to the waiter. He told me that the people are poor in Zimbabwe. They fought a long bush war before they were given independence. The war was bad for the country. The people suffered.

Zimbabwe became independent on the 18 April 1980. Robert Mugabe has been President since independence. The people of Zimbabwe still face many problems.

I drank my beer. It was cold and good. Then I went to find a Kentucky. I bought a lot of chicken and chips. I remembered Vusi and Thandi because they like Kentucky so much.

I came back to the truck. I found some people had made a fire. They were playing loud music. There were women dancing. I went to join them. One man gave me a beer. It is not easy if you speak different languages. I could not talk to them. I got tired of smiling. I went back to the truck. There was nowhere to wash so I took my water bottle and my cloth and I washed outside.

It takes me a long time to write all these new things. I must sleep now.

Wednesday, Zimbabwe

I found the place to offload the spare parts for cars that I had brought to Zimbabwe. When we were finished I drove north west to Chirundu.

The road from Harare to Chirundu is long and straight. The sun was already hot. I saw the sign to Lake Kariba, but I could not see the water. Near the sign to Kariba, big birds dived at my truck. I did not know why. The birds were like the yellow-billed kites we get in Durban. I do not like to kill things, but it is dangerous to turn the truck. I was happy when they flew off. I enjoyed driving over the mountain pass to Chirundu. I drove slowly keeping to the left hand side. I saw a family of jackals at the side of the road. They quickly ran into the bush. I saw some big kudu eating in the bush. I thought this was how the land was before too many people came. Now there are just fences everywhere and most of the animals are dead. I want everyone to live in peace with their neighbours, people and animals.

I parked at the garage in Chirundu where I found two other drivers. We walked through the trees to the little hotel. It looked cool and pretty. In the shade of tall trees were huts and a camping ground.

The toilets at the camping ground were dirty and smelly and there was no water. We walked to the hotel where it was cleaner. It was too hot inside so we sat in the garden near the swimming pool. The pool was more like a small dam because it was green. We asked for beers and hamburgers. While we were resting, an elephant came out of the bush and walked towards the pool. I was very afraid. My friends did not see it. When the elephant was near the pool I got up.

"Hey, man," I said, "let's go. Can't you see the elephant?"

The one called Nkululeko held my arm. "Relax, my friend," he said. "Some elephants come here to drink every night. They won't worry us."

I did not want to look stupid, so I sat down again although I was very nervous. I was ready to run if the elephant came nearer. This big animal walked slowly to the edge, stopped, sniffed the grass here and there, then put his trunk into the water. He sucked a lot of water into his trunk, and then he curled his trunk around and squirted the water into his mouth. I had never seen such a thing. I did not talk to the others. Instead, I watched the elephant.

After a while, he squirted the water over his back. I laughed to see this. Then the elephant turned around and went back into the bush. He did not make a sound. A person who came into the garden now would not even know an elephant had been there.

I am going to sleep well tonight and dream of my family.

Thursday, Zambia

This morning I found that the border post was quite small and not so busy. It opened at 6am. Soon I was in Zambia. I did not know what to expect. There were beautiful hills, full of green trees and a road full of potholes winding up and down the hills. I saw very few people. Now and then I saw a village in among the trees, with a bit of space cleared for planting. I drove for a long time without seeing another car.

I knew when I was coming to Lusaka, because the farms got bigger and there were many houses.

Outside the town there was a township of thousands and thousands of shacks.

"Hey! Just like home!" I thought.

I drove into the town. It was a small, poor place compared with Harare and Durban. There were some tall buildings. Most of the shops looked like trading stores or cafés. The streets were full of beggars. I asked where I should take my cargo.

I got good directions. I found the place and offloaded the maize from the truck. It took a long time.

Afterwards I found a noisy place that sold food and drink, and I sat down to rest. I was happy to be in Lusaka although Zambia felt very far away from Durban. While I was eating, some people tried to sell me things: watches, cigarettes, school books, fruit. I read my book so that they would not worry me. I read:

> Zambia became independent on 24 October 1964. The first president was Kenneth Kaunda. He was President until 1991 when the first multi-party elections were held, and President Chiluba was voted into power. After the 2001 election Levy Mwanawasa became chief of state.
>
> Zambia has not had civil war like Angola, Zimbabwe, Mozambique and South Africa, but it is still a poor country. It was a rich country because of the copper mines. When the copper price fell, the country became poor. Many farmers are struggling, and many people cannot find jobs.

DEMOCRATIC REPUBLIC OF THE CONGO (DRC)

ANGOLA

Busanga
Swamp

ZAMBIA

Livingstone

NAMIBIA

28

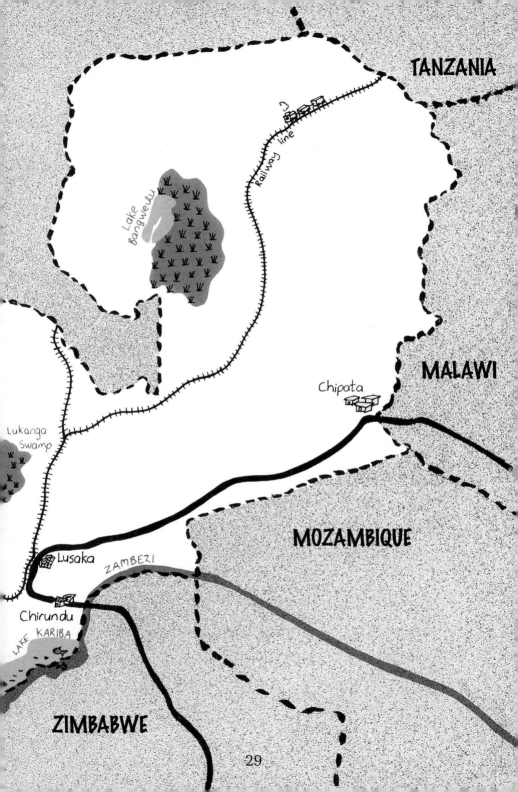

TANZANIA

MALAWI

Railway line

Lake Bangweulu

Chipata

Lukanga Swamp

MOZAMBIQUE

Lusaka

ZAMBEZI

Chirundu

LAKE KARIBA

ZIMBABWE

Zambia is a large country, and many tourists enjoy the big game parks.

I ate my food, got in my truck and drove off again. This time I drove east towards Malawi and the border post at Chipata. I drove for hours and hours. I drove across a big bridge over a wide, slow river. There was a sign which said:

```
No stopping
No photographs
Speed limit 5 km
```

This was Luangwa Beit Bridge. I did not know this river. I obeyed the signs although there was no one in sight. When I had crossed the bridge there was a STOP sign. I stopped. I did not know why, because there were no other cars on the road. When I drove on, I saw some soldiers at the top of the hill. I thought they must have seen me stop.

I drove for a few more hours. I looked for a garage or a place to stop, but there was nothing. At last I saw a sign.

It said:

> **Fresh Petrol**
> **Cold Drinks**
> **Iced Water**
> **Clean Toilets**
> **2km**

I was so happy. When I got there, the people were smiling and friendly. "Fill up please," I said.

"Sorry," they said, "no petrol."

"Oh!" I was puzzled. "Can I have a cold drink?"

"Sorry," said the man, "no cold drinks." He was still smiling and friendly.

"Ooops," I said. "How about some iced water?"

The woman said, "Sorry, we have not had water for two weeks."

Before I could ask about the toilet she said, "Come I will take you to our house. The toilets here are not working."

After visiting her house, I went on my way again.

Every now and then, I passed villages. There were women at the side of the road selling things. At first I did not know what they were. Then I saw they were mushrooms. They were not mushrooms like we get at home under the trees in the field after the rain. Oh no! These were very big mushrooms. Some were as big as a plate and some were even bigger. Most of them were cream coloured but some were brown. There were also smaller mushrooms: red and white and bright yellow. I don't like mushrooms so I did not stop.

It was late before I reached the border between Zambia and Malawi. It was still open. I did not want to fill in forms, because I was tired and hungry and dirty. I thought if the officials were also tired, they would let me through quickly.

I was lucky, but I still had to go through the Malawian side. I was cross and very hungry by the time I finished. It was too late to go on. I did not know where to get food, and I did not know where to sleep. I stopped at a big garage.

A man said I could sleep there if I left before the boss came in the morning. He gave me some cold water to wash with.

I am very tired, but I wrote this diary for you, my children.

Friday, Malawi

I left the garage very early. I saw some children selling bananas and some other things on the road. I stopped. I found my Malawian money, called kwachas, and bought some bananas. They were very big bananas and I was very hungry. The child said she also had dried fish. She called it "sipo". I don't like fish. I like phutu and meat.

The road to Lilongwe is narrow. The truck took up the whole road. When I saw a car coming, I did not know what to do. I saw the car going half off the road. I did that also. There was very little space and too many cars. I drove with only the right hand side of the truck on the tar and the wheels on the left side were in the dirt.

There were houses and little villages all the way to Lilongwe. As soon as I saw a "Coke" sign I stopped. I knew that was a café. I bought a warm Coke and a packet of chips. The chips tasted dusty and I asked how long they had been there. I did not know whether the Coke had come from far away in a big truck like mine, or whether it was bottled in Malawi.

At Lilongwe I found the place for my cargo. They were waiting for me. They told me to leave my truck there and come back the next morning when it would be reloaded with fruit and maize for Mozambique. I did not know what to do without my truck. Luckily another truck driver saw me.

"Are you a new boy?" he asked. He had a very dark skin and modern sunglasses. He spoke in a way I had never heard before. He had a small vest and big muscles so I didn't tell him not to call me boy.

His name was Pierre. He took me to a cheap place to sleep. We walked a long way through the city. There are some big hotels in Lilongwe and some big trading stores. Pierre took me to a rest house where there were many other truck drivers. He spoke to them in a language I had never heard before. I asked him where he came from and what language he spoke.

Pierre said, "I am from the Democratic Republic of the Congo, and we are speaking French, South African boy."

DEMOCRATIC REPUBLIC OF THE CONGO (DRC)

ZAMBIA

Lusaka

Chirundu

Harare

ZIMBABWE

TANZANIA

LAKE MALAWI

Chipata

MALAWI

Lilongwe

MOZAMBIQUE

Blantyre

His two friends laughed. They said they were not working in the Democratic Republic of the Congo any more, only driving the Tanzania to Malawi route. There were some other drivers there: one from Zambia, one from Mozambique and some Malawians. I felt I was part of a big world of truck drivers. The Malawians took me to a place to buy meat. We made a fire and ate well. There was music and dancing. Some women came to the party. One by one the men went away with a woman.

I remembered that the truck drivers in Durban call this route, "The Slow Road to Hell", because so many drivers have got AIDS and are dying slowly. I went to my small bed. I looked at Malawi in my map book. Malawi is a small narrow country. On the map, Lake Malawi takes up most of the country. It is a very big lake. This is what I read in my book:

> The lake is so big that it looks like the sea. When the wind blows there are waves. If there is a storm the waves can get big and turn boats over. Many Malawians work at the lake. They catch many fish. Some fish are dried, some

frozen, some sold fresh. There are also many farmers in Malawi. They grow maize, fruit, tea and trees for rubber.

Lilongwe is the capital city of Malawi. It is the home of the government. Dr Kamuzu Banda was Life President from independence in 1964 until 1994 when Bakili Muluzi won the first multi-party elections. Muluzi stood down at the elections in mid-2004. His successor is Dr Bingu wa Mutharika in a coalition with opposition parties.

I wrote this in my diary for you. Now I am going to sleep.

Saturday, Malawi

I went to fetch my truck. It was ready and the man showed me the road to Blantyre. The road was busy. There were many government and private cars, donkey carts, people riding bicycles and walking. There were women and children selling big bananas and mangoes. I bought some. They were cheap and tasty. It is a long way from Lilongwe to Blantyre. I did not mind because there were many things to see. The land changed near Blantyre. It was cooler. Blantyre is older than Lilongwe and has more people. It is the old capital. I liked it more.

I had only one crate to offload in Blantyre and some papers to hand over. It did not take long. Soon I was driving towards the Mozambique border.

When I got to the border, they said I must wait until the morning when all the cars and trucks would go together. That is where I am now, at the Mozambique border. There are some other truck drivers here. We are all going to sleep in our trucks.

I hardly spoke to anyone. I have just stayed in my truck. I ate my fruit and bread. I bought the bread at the PTC, the People's Trading Centre. There are many PTCs in Malawi. I have made coffee on the gas stove, and I am going to try to sleep.

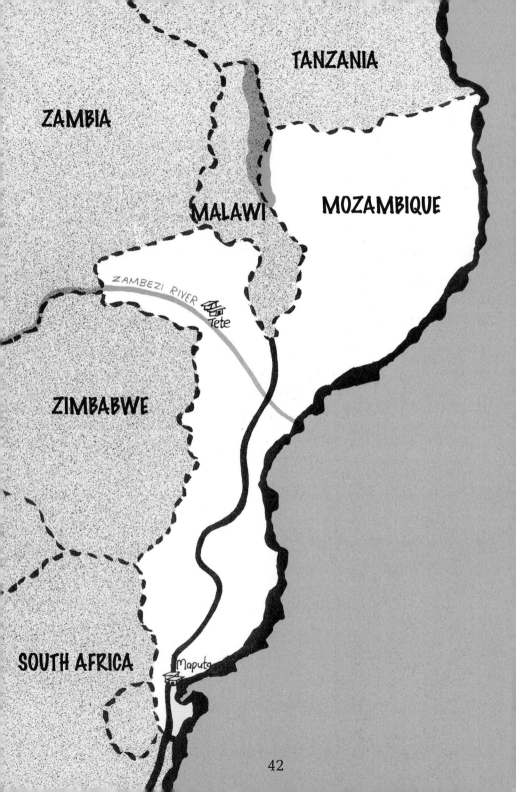

ZAMBIA

TANZANIA

MALAWI

MOZAMBIQUE

ZAMBEZI RIVER

Tete

ZIMBABWE

SOUTH AFRICA

Maputo

Sunday, Mozambique

I was so happy when I got to Maputo. I stopped at the sea. I do not smoke, but when some children came up to me selling cigarettes, I bought some. I also bought matches. I saw that the cigarettes and matches were made in Maputo. I thought there must be some factories in Maputo. There are many palm trees along the road next to the sea. There are places where you can sit and rest. I did that. I walked and rested, walked and rested for a long way.

I found a market place. There were people sitting drinking beer and eating. It looked good. The waiter spoke only Portuguese. I waited until he brought someone a hamburger. I pointed to the hamburger. He pointed to fish and prawns. I shook my head. I pointed at the hamburger again. He knew what I wanted.

I left the place with a full stomach. I am staying at the municipal caravan park because they allow trucks to park there. It was good to have a cold water shower and feel clean again. I have put my blankets on the grass next to the truck. I am going to sleep outside because it is hot. The air is warm and sticky like Durban. Even the trees and the flowers are the same as Durban. Only some buildings and the language are different.

Sleep well, my children, I will soon be home.

Monday, Mozambique

I spent the day near the docks and in town.
The place where I had to offload was very slow.
They told me to come back later.

I walked to the market. There were lots of
things to buy. There were many people at the
market. At the one end there were many
different kinds of bread for sale. Round and
long loaves and rolls. I did not want to buy
anything until I had had a good look around.
There were tables of fish: big fish, small fish,
mussels, oysters, crabs and prawns. I don't like
the smell or the look of those things. I walked
past quickly. I went to the vegetables. That was
nice. There were all sorts of vegetables: green
peppers, tomatoes, onions. There were small
coloured birds in cages, and some were
singing. There were tables with groceries: soap
powder, tinned milk, rice – everything. Some of
the tins were the same as in South Africa.
Some were different and came from eastern
Europe and Asia. There were lots and lots of
cashew nuts: in tins, in plastic bags, raw,
roasted and flavoured. I bought some for my
friends and family.

I bought rolls for lunch. I could not find any Rama or polony or cheese. I bought tomatoes instead. Outside the market, on every street corner, people sat selling things: sweets, cigarettes, matches, beer, fruit, cashew nuts. I found two teenagers selling butter. It was very expensive, but I bought some. There was loud township jazz coming from some of the cafés. Many people were sitting outside at tables on the pavement drinking and eating.

I sat at a café and read my book. Things have been difficult in Mozambique. This is what I read:

> Mozambique has been independent since 1975. Most of the Portuguese colonisers left the country. They did not train people to take their places, so the country has suffered. The first President, Samora Machel, struggled to rebuild the country. The Mozambique National Resistance (the MNR or Renamo) took up arms against the government. They were helped by outside countries. There was a long and bad war, which ended in 1992.

From 1986 to 2004 Joaquim Chissano
was President. He was succeeded by
Armando Guebuza.

I went to check on my truck. The people there
said I should leave tomorrow. Then I can go
straight through to Durban in daylight. The
one who speaks English asked me to sleep at
his house.

I went with him to his house which is in the
informal area on the way to the airport. It looks
like Inanda. His wife and three children
greeted me. She told me they used to have a
good farm in the country, but it was burnt down
in the war, and her brother and his children
were shot. After that, she and her family moved
into town. Now she does hairdressing, and her
husband managed to find a job.

They were pleased to hear about South Africa.
They gave me warm water to wash with, and
then I sat at the table to write my diary in the
candlelight. I am going home tomorrow.

Tuesday, South Africa

I left early this morning. The land was dry and bare. I crossed the border quickly. The land was also dry on the South African side. But I was happy to be back where I understood the language. As I drove towards Durban the land became greener. It had rained.

Then I saw the sugar cane. I knew I was not far from home. Phutu and meat for supper I thought.

And when I got home, I was right.

Tower Hamlets

Suppliers Code	AVA
Price	£ 3·75
Invoice Date	01/11/2006
LOC	BOW
Class	428·6
Barcode	C001278856

Tower Hamlets

Thanks

We thank the following people for their help in evaluating this book:

Lucy Chambers and Anne Macdonald of the Centre for Adult Education at the University of Natal in Pietermaritzburg;

Anton Vusimuzi Buthelezi, Owen Erik Dlamini, David Fana Maseko, Vincent Lolie Ngcobo and Louise Mensing from Umgeni Water English learners' group.

NEW READERS PUBLISHERS

New Readers Publishers of the Centre for Adult Education, School of Adult and Higher Education, University of KwaZulu-Natal, Durban, develops and supports adult literacy and basic English Second Language skills by producing books in simple language for the entertainment and education of adults.

How to contact us

If you want to find out more about New Readers Publishers or about other books that we publish, please contact:

New Readers Publishers
Centre for Adult Education
School of Adult and Higher Education
University of KwaZulu-Natal
Durban
4041

Telephone: 031 – 2602568
Fax: 031 – 2601168
E-mail: keyser@ukzn.ac.za
Website: www.nrp.ukzn.ac.za

The diary of Thami the truck driver

First published 1992 by
New Readers Publishers
Centre for Adult Education
School of Adult and Higher Education
University of KwaZulu-Natal, Durban, 4041
South Africa

Cover illustration by Trisha Campbell
Design and desktop publication by Lesley Lewis of Inkspots
Printed by Pinetown Printers, Pinetown

Reprinted: 1995
Revised edition: 2005

ISBN: 1-874897-75-1